CAHIER D'EXERCICES

Fourth Edition

FRENCH
IS FUN

Book 1

Gail Stein
Former Teacher
Foreign Language Department
New York City Schools

Heywood Wald, Ph.D.
Former Assistant Principal
Foreign Language Department
Martin Van Buren High School
New York City

AMSCO

AMSCO SCHOOL PUBLICATIONS, INC.
315 Hudson Street, New York, N.Y. 10013

PREFACE

This CAHIER D'EXERCICES supplements the practice materials in FRENCH IS FUN, BOOK 1, FOURTH EDITION. The vocabulary and structural elements are closely coordinated with parallel chapters in the textbook.

While some exercises use techniques similar to those in the basal text, others extend the range of the materials. The workbook format provides opportunity for writing practice and intensive homework.

The pages are perforated to permit the collection of home or class assignments.

Cover design by Lisa Delgado

Cover art © Images.com/Corbis

Illustrations by Edward Malsberg/Noel Malsberg

Electronic composition by Northeastern Graphic, Inc.

Please visit our Web site at: **www.amscopub.com**

When ordering this book, please specify *either*
R 690 W *or* CAHIER, FRENCH IS FUN, BOOK 1, 4th Edition

ISBN: 978-1-56765-344-1
NYC Item: 56765-344-0

Copyright © 2011, 2003, 1991 by Amsco School Publications, Inc.

Contents

Leçon 1

A. Express what you can see in Marie-Claire's room besides the furniture.

1. _____   6. _____

2. _____   7. _____

3. _____   8. _____

4. _____   9. _____

5. _____   10. _____

B. Today you went to see a movie with a friend. List four adjectives that describe the movie.

1. _____   3. _____

2. _____   4. _____

C. The Maréchals are tourists in your city. Identify the places they saw.

1. _____

2. _____

3. _____

4. _____

5. _____

6. _____

7. _____

8. _____

9. _____ **10.** _____

D. Identify what you like or don't like from the list below.

cinéma	**musique rock**	**école**
leçon	**télévision**	**professeur**
docteur	**danse**	**sport**

EXAMPLE: **J'aime le docteur. / Je n'aime pas le docteur.**

1. _____

2. _____

3. _____

4. _____

5. _____

6. _____

7. _____

8. _____

E. Give your opinion of each item by choosing from the list of adjectives given.

intelligent	**nécessaire**	**confortable**
excellent	**délicieux**	**américain**
populaire	**horrible**	**élégant**

1. Le fruit est_____.

2. Le pull-over est _____.

   3. L'accident est _____.

   4. Le programme est_____.

   5. L'appartement est_____.

   6. L'acteur est _____.

   7. Le vocabulaire est _____.

   8. Le président est_____.

F. Roland works at the flea market. He has to change all the signs to show that more than one of each item is being sold. Write the changes that he will have to make.

   EXAMPLE: la table   **les tables**

   1. la guitare _____

   2. l'animal _____

   3. l'automobile _____

   4. le fruit _____

   5. le stylo _____

   6. le journal _____

   7. le bureau _____

   8. la télévision _____

G. Look at each picture and tell how you feel about the thing(s) shown

J'adore *(I love)*   **Je n'aime pas** *(I don't like)*
J'aime *(I like)*   **Je déteste** *(I detest)*

EXAMPLES:

J'aime l'école.

Je n'aime pas les chiens.

1.
   _____

2.
   _____

3.
   _____

4.
   _____

5.
   _____

6.
   _____

7. _____

8. _____

LA VIE PRATIQUE

Select the best answer to the question based on what you read, and write its number in the space provided.

What's missing from this list of French achievements?   _____

1. fashion
2. cars
3. computers
4. perfumes

Leçon 2

A. Identify what Pierre is looking at in school.

EXAMPLE: **Il regarde** *(He is looking at)* **le bureau.**

1. _____

2. _____

3. _____

4. _____

5. _____

6. _____

7. _____

8. _____

9. _____

10. _____

B. Describe the people and things in your classroom.

drôle	**sympathique**	**difficile**
intéressant	**grand**	**noir**
moderne	**immense**	

1. L'élève est _____ .

2. Le dictionnaire est _____ .

3. Le professeur est _____ .

4. Le livre est _____ .

5. Le tableau est _____ .

6. L'exercice est _____ .

7. Le bureau est _____ .

8. Le crayon est _____ .

C. Write a list of six things you always have in your school bag.

1. _____   4. _____

2. _____   5. _____

3. _____   6. _____

D. There are 16 school-related items hidden in the puzzle. Circle the words from left to right, right to left, up or down, or diagonally.

D	C	B	U	A	C	B	U	R	E	A	U
E	I	Y	R	C	R	A	Y	O	N	N	O
E	L	C	E	F	P	R	H	R	C	E	E
É	Y	S	T	T	E	D	E	I	R	L	C
L	T	O	T	I	D	L	P	T	E	E	T
È	V	U	P	Y	O	R	Ê	A	B	R	A
V	D	A	D	C	L	N	O	N	L	E	B
E	P	P	É	I	E	O	N	A	I	B	L
U	B	V	O	F	A	G	E	A	F	E	E
L	L	I	V	R	E	N	R	T	I	R	A
R	È	G	L	E	T	C	T	V	E	R	U
A	R	U	E	S	S	E	F	O	R	P	E

E. Express what classes these students attend.

EXAMPLE: **la classe de maths.**

1. _____

2. _____

3. _____

$$\left(\tfrac{1}{2}x^3 + x^2 + \tfrac{1}{2}\right) \circ \left(x^2 - 2x + 4\right)$$

4. _____

5. _____

6. _____

7. _____

8. _____

F. Match the command with the picture.

Écoutez!   **Ouvrez le livre!**
Fermez le livre!   **Écrivez!**
Levez la main!   **Corrigez l'exercice!**
Lisez!   **Asseyez-vous!**

1. _____

2. _____

3. _____

4. _____

5. _____

6. _____

7. _____

8. _____

G. Supply the correct indefinite article (**un, une**, or **des**) to identify whom or what you see while walking in the city.

1. _____ animaux

2. _____ restaurant

3. _____ artistes

4. _____ maison

5. _____ boutique

6. _____ jardins

7. _____ parc

8. _____ cafés

9. _____ hôtel

10. _____ cinéma

11. _____ vendeurs

12. _____ automobiles

H. Write what Janine finds while looking in an old trunk in the attic.

EXAMPLE: **Elle trouve** *(She finds)* **une télévision.**

1. _____

2. _____

3. _____

4. _____

5. _____

6. _____

7. _____

8. _____

9. _____

10. _____

11. _____

12. _____

13. _____

14. _____

15. _____

LA VIE PRATIQUE

Select the best answer to the question based on what you read, and write its number in the space provided.

ECOLE UNIVERS DES ENFANTS
Institution privée d'enseignement
préscolaire et primaire.
– Bonne formation en langues arabe,
française et anglaise, et en informatique.
– Une bonne équipe pédagogique,
effectifs limités permettant un
encadrement efficace et un suivi
personnalisé.

What will the students in this school learn?   _____

   1. Italian
   2. Advanced Mathematics
   3. Computer Science
   4. Geography

Leçon 3

A. Express in dollars how much it costs to do each of the following activities.

EXAMPLE: go to the movies ($9.00) **Ça coûte neuf dollars.**

1. buy a slice of pizza ($3.00) _____

2. buy a hamburger and fries ($6.00) _____

3. rent a video ($5.00) _____

4. buy two ice cream cones ($7.00) _____

5. go to an amusement park ($19.00) _____

6. buy a compact disk ($16.00) _____

7. buy three comic books ($12.00) _____

8. play ten video games ($10.00) _____

B. Express how many people there are in each family.

EXAMPLE: Les Dupont/17 **Il y a dix-sept personnes.**

1. Les Martin/15 _____

2. Les Caron/24 _____

3. Les Lesage/9 _____

4. Les Renoir/13 _____

5. Les Dubois/11 _____

6. Les Ricard/3 _____

C. Write the problems from Josette's math book and answer them in French.

EXAMPLE: 10 + 3 = **Dix et trois font treize.**

1. 12 + 2 = _____

2. 30 − 9 = _____

3. 20 ÷ 4 = _____

4. 3 × 8 = _____

5. 6 + 5 = _____

6. 15 ÷ 5 = _____

7. 27 − 8 = _____

8. 7 × 2 = _____

D. Write these French phone numbers in French.

1. 01.45.13.49.24 _____

2. 04.48.68.81.92 _____

3. 02.47.36.16.57 _____

4. 06.43.75.18.89 _____

5. 01.46.41.91.26 _____

6. 02.40.33.67.79 _____

7. 05.42.52.99.74 _____

8. 03.49.80.01.44 _____

E. Write out how far each student lives from Paris.

EXAMPLE: Nancy/27 km.   **vingt-sept kilomètres**

1. Julien/39 km _____.

2. Sylvie/67 km _____.

3. André/90 km _____.

4. Renée/43 km _____.

5. Robert/51 km _____.

6. Lise/83 km _____.

7. Roger/100 km _____.

8. Claire/77 km _____.

F. A French radio announcer is reading off the numbers of the following winning tickets. Write them in French.

1. LOTERIE NATIONALE 10 33 54 _____
_____
_____

2. LOTERIE NATIONALE 17 96 81 _____
_____
_____

3. LOTERIE NATIONALE 75 20 66 _____
_____
_____

4. LOTERIE NATIONALE 41 90 50 _____
_____
_____

5. LOTERIE NATIONALE 15 25 79 _____
_____
_____

6.

LOTERIE NATIONALE
88   39   12

_____

_____

_____

G. Write in French how much each person earns per day.

EXAMPLE: Marie/100 **Marie gagne cent euros par jour.**

1. Christian/66 _____

2. Denise/96 _____

3. Philippe/72 _____

4. Rachel/54 _____

5. Simon/98 _____

6. Charline/84 _____

H. Write a list of the last five things you bought and their prices in French.

1. _____

2. _____

3. _____

4. _____

5. _____

I. Antoine is a teller in a French bank. Express how he would write these dollar amounts the French way.

EXAMPLE: $2,358.22 **2.358,22 dollars**

1. $1,746.70 _____

2. $50,800.62 _____

3. $388,217.15 _____

4. $1,525,682.38 _____

J. Label the cost of the following school supplies.

Example: **cinq dollars**

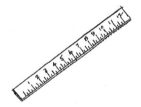

1. _____   **2.** _____

3. _____   **4.** _____

5. _____   **6.** _____

K. You are going to buy school supplies. Write a note in French to a friend using numbers to explain what you need

EXAMPLE: **Il me faut** *(I need)* **deux cahiers.**

_____

_____

_____

_____

LA VIE PRATIQUE

Select the best answer to the question based on what you read, and write its letter in the space provided.

Which book title contains the largest number?   _____

    a. Blanche-Neige et les sept nains
    b. Mille et une nuits
    c. Vingt mille lieues sous les mers
    d. Cent un dalmatiens

Leçon 4

A. M. Roland has important meetings with people all day long. He frequently asks his co-workers for the time. Write out their responses.

EXAMPLE: 7:15   **Il est sept heures et quart.**

1. 8:30 _____

2. 9:15 _____

3. 10:45 _____

4. 11:20 _____

5. 12:35 _____

6. 1:55 _____

7. 2:05 _____

8. 2:50 _____

B. Write at what time each of these teens wakes up on the weekend.

EXAMPLE: Anne/7:05   **à sept heures cinq**

1. Nathalie/6:55 _____

2. Roger/1:15 _____

3. Lise/10:25 _____

4. Thierry/12:30 _____

5. Claudette/11:35 _____

6. Paul/8:45 _____

7. Liliane/9:10 _____

8. Georges/2:30 _____

C. Write out in French at what time you can see the following shows.

20.30   Fletch aux trousses

Film américain de Michael Ritchie
Durée: 1 h 35. Policier. Rediffusion le 13 octobre.

DISTRIBUTION: Chevy Chase, Joe Don Baker.

L'HISTOIRE - Un riche homme d'affaires propose un marché sordide à Fletch.

22.05   Flash d'informations

22.10   Bobagolfoot
«FOOTBALL»

Présenté par Pierre Sled. Réalisé par Jérôme Revon. Produit par Charles Biétry.

*le match anglais de la semaine (10 mn)*Un match de championnat étranger (10 mn)*Tous les buts de la deuxième division et un match de deuxième division (10 mn)*

22.40   Boxe à Baltard

Commentaires de Jean-Philippe Lustyk et Jean-Claude Bouttier. Réalisé par Jean-Paul Jaud.

Réunion internationale au pavillon Baltard avec notamment: Limarola, Belbouli et Fontana.

0.10   Football américain

(Rediffusion du 9 octobre)

1.05   King Kong II

Film américain de John Guillermin
Durée: 1 h 21. Aventures. Rediffusion le 11 octobre

DISTRIBUTION: Peter Elliot. Georges Yiasomi.

L'HISTOIRE - Sorti de son coma à la suite d'une opération, King Kong part à la recherche d'un gorille femelle.

1. the news _____

_____

2. a police film _____

_____

3. a soccer match _____

_____

4. an adventure film _____

_____

5. a football game _____

_____

6. a boxing match _____

_____

D. Write a list of four television programs you watch during the week and at what time you watch them.

1. _____

2. _____

3. _____

4. _____

E. Look at this official French train schedule. Express the departure times in conventional forms.

NICE 18h19
ANTIBES 18h40
ST-TROPEZ 19h25
CANNES 19h58
TOULON 20h46
MARSEILLE. 21h47
AVIGNON 23h01
VALENCE 0h08
PARIS 2h25

EXAMPLE: Nice/18h19
            Nice/à six heures dix-neuf

1. _____

2. _____

3. _____

4. _____

5. _____

6. _____

7. _____

8. _____

F. Express the following as official times.

EXAMPLE: 1:15 p.m.   **13h15**

1. 2.05 p.m. _____

2. 9:30 p.m. _____

3. 4:35 p.m. _____

4. 6:10 p.m. _____

5. 3:20 p.m. _____

6. 11:00 p.m. _____

7. 12:25 a.m. _____

8. 5:45 p.m. _____

9. 1:35 p.m. _____

10. 7:40 p.m. _____

11. 8:50 p.m. _____

12. 10:55 p.m. _____

LA VIE PRATIQUE

DINER
70€

TOUT COMPRIS/*ALL INCLUDED*

DÎNER DE LUXE HABILLÉ
STRICT EXIGÉ
(TIE AND JACKET COMPULSORY)
ENFANTS DÉCONSEILLÉS
DÉPART TLJ À 20 H 30
DURÉE : 2 H 15
(du 15/11 au 15/3, fermé le lundi)

☎ **RÉSERVER** (impératif)

At what time do you return from this cruise?   _____

1. At 8:30
2. At 2:15
3. At 10:45
4. At 9:00

Leçon 5

A. Match the verb with the noun that could be used to express what people did at Lucien's party.

1. goûter   _____

2. regarder   _____

3. écouter   _____

4. chanter   _____

5. danser   _____

6. jouer   _____

7. gagner   _____

8. parler   _____

a. des CD
b. le disco
c. un prix (*a prize*)
d. le dessert
e. «Joyeux anniversaire»
   (*Happy Birthday*)
f. français
g. dans le jardin
h. un film

B. Write the pronoun you would use (**tu** or **vous**) if you were speaking to these people.

1. un enfant   _____

2. le père de Richard   _____

3. Valérie et André   _____

4. le président   _____

5. Georges   _____

6. ta (*your*) sœur   _____

C. Write the pronoun you could use to substitute for each noun.

1. Hélène _____

2. Michel et Éric _____

3. Lisette et Jacques _____

4. Mme Restaud _____

5. Paul _____

6. les docteurs _____

7. le livre _____

8. la porte et la fenêtre _____

9. la craie _____

10. les dictionnaires _____

D. Write what these people do in their spare time.

EXAMPLE: Je/écouter la radio   **J'écoute la radio.**

1. André/travailler à son (*his*) auto

   _____

2. Je/regarder la télévision

   _____

3. Alice et Sylvie/écouter des CD

   _____

4. Tu/préparer un dessert délicieux

   _____

5. Ils/chanter

   _____

6. Nous/jouer au football

_____

7. Vous/danser à la discothèque

_____

8. Elles/marcher dans le parc

_____

9. Il/penser à son amie

_____

10. Elle/parler au téléphone

_____

11. Catherine/jouer du piano

_____

12. Nous/regarder des films

_____

E. Fill in the correct form of a verb that makes sense in the sentence, choosing from the list below.

aimer	**donner**	**fermer**	**inviter**	**préparer**
arriver	**entrer**	**habiter**	**penser**	**trouver**

1. Tu _____ dans la classe.

2. Le professeur _____ la fenêtre.

3. René _____ le dictionnaire à Roland.

4. Georgette _____ beaucoup Paul.

5. Les élèves _____ à l'école.

6. Alain _____ ses (*his*) amis à une surprise-partie.

7. J' _____ New York.

8. Nous _____ la mousse au chocolat.

9. Vous _____ le livre.

10. Elles _____ à (*about*) l'examen.

F. Write a list of five things you do in your spare time.

1. _____

2. _____

3. _____

4. _____

5. _____

G. Your friend Marie tells you what she does and asks if you do the same. Give a negative answer to her questions.

EXAMPLE: Je joue au tennis. Et toi *(and you)?*
Je ne joue pas au tennis.

1. J'habite un appartement. Et toi?

_____

2. J'aime le golf. Et toi?

_____

3. J'arrive à l'école en retard (*late*). Et toi?

_____

4. Je gagne beaucoup d'argent (*money*). Et toi?

_____

5. Je travaille après (*after*) l'école. Et toi?

_____

6. Je parle italien. Et toi?

_____

H. Write what some students in your class don't do.

EXAMPLE: Jean/penser à l'école
Jean ne pense pas à l'école.

1. André/danser bien

_____

2. les filles/chanter beaucoup

_____

3. nous/inviter le professeur au cinéma

_____

4. Luc et Paul/parler souvent au téléphone

_____

5. Anne/jouer au tennis

_____

6. je/préparer le dîner

_____

7. elle/travailler dur (*hard*)

_____

8. tu/écouter la musique rock

_____

9. vous/regarder les programmes de sport

_____

10. les garçons/marcher dans le parc

_____

I. Use **Est-ce-que** to change all the statements to questions.

1. Ils cherchent un hôtel confortable.

_____

2. Tu joues bien au base-ball.

_____

3. Elles invitent les garçons.

_____

4. Vous arrivez en France avec Marie.

_____

5. Tu prépares un dîner délicieux.

_____

6. Ils travaillent dans la boutique.

_____

7. Elles trouvent un bon *(good)* restaurant.

_____

8. Vous gagnez le match.

_____

9. Nous visitons la France.

_____

10. Il chante à l'école.

_____

J. You are writing your first letter to a French pen pal. Use **Est-ce que** to express the questions you ask

EXAMPLE: habiter Paris

Est-ce que tu habites Paris?

1. aimer l'école

_____

2. écouter la musique rock

_____

3. travailler après l'école

_____

4. regarder beaucoup la télévision

_____

5. préparer le dîner pour ta famille

_____

6. danser avec tes amis

_____

K. Now ask your pen pal the questions you really would like to ask, using **Est-ce que** or intonation.

1. _____

2. _____

3. _____

4. _____

5. _____

6. _____

LA VIE PRATIQUE

Select the best answer to the question based on what you read, and write its number in the space provided.

Qu'est-ce que tu peux faire ici?   _____

   1. écouter un concert
   2. jouer avec des animaux
   3. regarder des plantes
   4. jouer au football

Nom: _____ Classe: _____ Date: _____

Leçon 6

A. Identify Marc Dupont's relatives.

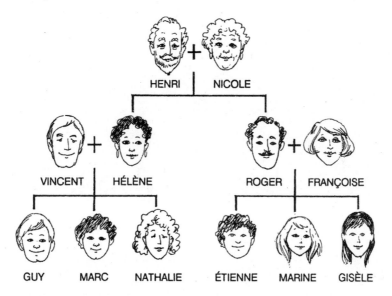

1. Vincent est **le père de Marc.**

2. Henri est _____.

3. Nicole est _____.

4. Guy est _____.

5. Hélène est _____.

6. Françoise est _____.

7. Roger est _____.

8. Gisèle est _____.

9. Étienne est _____.

10. Nathalie est _____.

33

B. Look at the picture and identify all the people at the reunion (Use as many plurals as possible.)

1. _____

2. _____

3. _____

4. _____

5. _____

6. _____

7. _____

8. _____

9. _____

10. _____

C. You are trying to explain family relationships to your young cousin. Tell how these people are related to you.

1. La mère de ma mère est _____.

2. Le frère de mon père est _____.

3. Le fils de mon oncle est_____.

4. La fille de mes parents est _____.

5. Le père de mon père est _____.

6. La sœur de mon père est_____.

7. La fille de ma tante est _____.

8. Le fils de mes parents est _____.

D. Express what everyone in the family is doing by filling in the blank with the possessive adjective that corresponds to the subject.

EXAMPLE: J'aime **ma** mère.

1. Il parle à _____ grand-mère.

2. Elles travaillent avec _____ parents.

3. Nous téléphonons à _____ famille.

4. Tu invites _____ cousin.

5. Ils cherchent un cadeau pour _____ mère.

6. J'habite avec _____ grands-parents.

7. Vous écrivez à _____ cousines.

8. Elle écoute _____ père.

9. Je prépare le dîner pour _____ parents et _____ sœur.

10. Les enfants jouent avec _____ oncle.

E. Change the expressions in bold type to the plural and make all other necessary changes.

EXAMPLES: Je parle avec **mon ami.**   **Je parle avec mes amis.**
            Sa sœur habite Paris.   **Ses sœurs habitent Paris.**

1. Ma cousine cherche **son livre.**

   _____

2. **Mon frère** écoute un concert.

   _____

3. **Notre oncle** travaille à New York.

   _____

4. L'élève étudie **sa leçon.**

   _____

5. Les garçons regardent **leur professeur.**

   _____

6. Je ne danse pas avec **son cousin.**

   _____

7. Tu cherches **ton cahier?**

   _____

8. **Votre sœur** ne parle pas beaucoup.

   _____

9. **Notre professeur** donne beaucoup de devoirs.

   _____

10. Tu fais **ton exercice?**

    _____

11. Je ne trouve pas **mon chat.**

    _____

12. Les filles parlent avec **leur amie.**

    _____

F. Use **sa**, **son**, **ses**, **leur**, or **leurs** to express possession by the people shown in the pictures.

EXAMPLE: **sa** classe

1. _____ maison

2. _____ famille

3. _____ journaux

4. _____ école

5. _____ bureau

6. _____ sandwich

7. _____ animaux

8. _____ professeurs

G. Use the correct form of the possessive adjective for each noun in parentheses to express the relationship between items or people mentioned.

EXAMPLE: mes frères (famille)   **ma famille**

1. ta maison (livres) _____

2. nos amis (sœur) _____

3. votre oncle (cousines) _____

4. son cahier (crayons) _____

5. leurs chats (chien) _____

6. ses chaussures (blouse) _____

7. notre école (professeurs) _____

8. ta radio (téléphone) _____

9. ma tante (oncles) _____

10. sa règle (dictionnaire) _____

H. Your French pen pal plans to come to visit you. Write him/her a note in French about your family.

_____

_____

_____

_____

_____

_____

LA VIE PRATIQUE

Select the best answer to the question based on what you read, and write its number in the space provided.

**LE DÉFI
ÉDUCATIF DE
LA MAIRIE**
**Paris aide ses petits
à devenir grands**

*Toutes les familles des
grandes villes se trouvent
tôt ou tard confrontées à
ce problème: comment
concilier les obligations et
les choix des parents avec le
rythme de vie des enfants,
comment occuper le temps
laissé libre après l'école?*

According to this newspaper clipping, what problem faces families who live in big cities?   _____

1. There is a shortage of housing.
2. Schools are overcrowded.
3. Large cities are dangerous.
4. How do you keep children busy after school?

Leçon 7

A. Identify these people in French.

EXAMPLE: **C'est une secrétaire.**

1. _____

2. _____

3. _____

4. _____

39

5. _____

6. _____

7. _____

8. _____

9. _____

10. _____

B. The people in your class are describing themselves and each other. Express what they say using the correct form of the verb **être** and the adjectives provided below.

aimable	dynamique	moderne	populaire
sociable	sincère	comique	formidable

EXAMPLE: **Elles sont comiques.**

1. Tu _____ .

2. Nous _____ .

3. Geneviève _____ .

4. Pierre et Christophe _____ .

5. Je _____ .

6. Brigitte _____ .

7. Vous_____ .

8. Guy _____ .

C. Yesterday your friend gave his opinion about some people. Today he is in a bad mood and has completely changed his mind. Rewrite all his thoughts in the negative.

EXAMPLE: Marc est intelligent.   **Marc n'est pas intelligent.**

1. Nous sommes petits. _____ .

2. L'actrice est jolie._____ .

3. Les artistes sont pauvres. _____ .

4. Je suis mince._____ .

5. L'agent de police est fort. _____ .

6. Vous êtes intéressants. _____ .

7. Les docteurs sont cruels._____ .

8. Tu es grand. _____ .

D. Write a letter in French to your new pen pal asking six questions about him/her.

_____

_____

_____

_____

_____

La Vie pratique

Select the best answer to the question based on what you read, and write its number in the space provided.

CLINIQUE BLOMET
recherche pour service de
CHIRURGIE

**INFIRMIÈRES
DE JOUR**

**INFIRMIÈRES
DE NUIT**

136 rue Blomet
75015 Paris
Mº CONVENTION

48.28.40.60

What job is being advertised?   _____

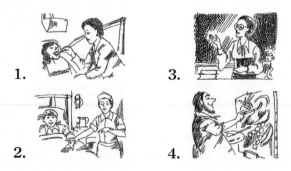

1.

2.

3.

4.

Leçon 8

A. Identify in French what Mme Watteau has hanging on her laundry line.

1. _____   5. _____

2. _____   6. _____

3. _____   7. _____

4. _____   8. _____

B. Identify what M. Legrand is packing into his suitcase.

1. _____   6. _____

2. _____   7. _____

3. _____   8. _____

4. _____   9. _____

5. _____   10. _____

C. Describe the clothing of the different people you see in your class picture.

EXAMPLE: jupe/Marie/super   **Sa jupe est super.**

1. chemise/Robert/ élégant _____.

2. tennis/Andrée/magnifique _____.

3. cravate/Michel/laid _____.

4. robe/Julie/ joli _____.

5. pantalon/Renée/long _____.

6. chaussures/Hélène/étroit _____.

7. ceinture/Daniel/parfait _____.

8. baskets/Julien/formidable _____.

D. Use the correct form of the adjectives to describe the people.

1. (blond) Madame Dubois, l'avocate, est _____.

2. (élégant) L'actrice, Audrey Tautou, est _____.

3. (amusant) Ma sœur Nicole est _____.

4. (timide) Mes frères Jean et Paul sont _____.

5. (important) Notre docteur est _____.

6. (brun) Notre mère est _____.

7. (américain) Ma grand-mère est _____.

8. (intéressant) Nos professeurs sont _____.

E. Write a list of five adjectives in French that describe you.

1. _____   **4.** _____

2. _____   **5.** _____

3. _____

F. Label the pairs of opposites.

1. _____   **2.** _____

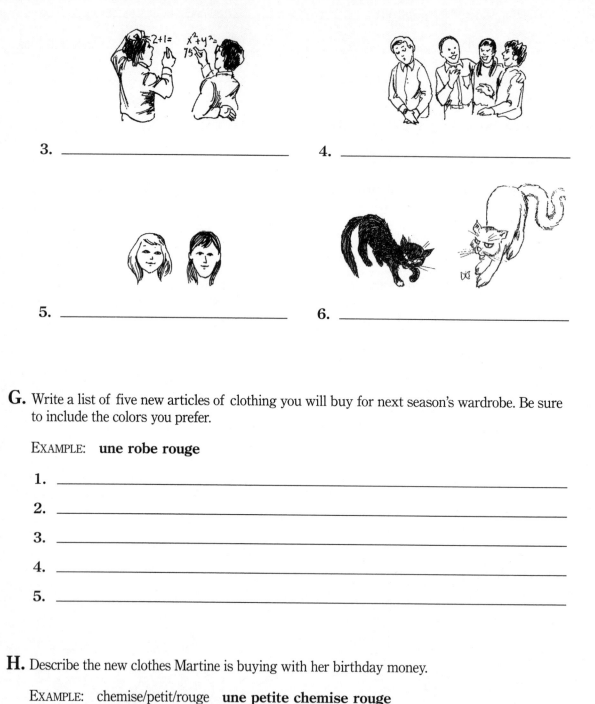

3. _____   4. _____

5. _____   6. _____

G. Write a list of five new articles of clothing you will buy for next season's wardrobe. Be sure to include the colors you prefer.

EXAMPLE: **une robe rouge**

1. _____

2. _____

3. _____

4. _____

5. _____

H. Describe the new clothes Martine is buying with her birthday money.

EXAMPLE: chemise/petit/rouge   **une petite chemise rouge**

1. chaussures/joli/rouge _____

2. pull-over/grand/élégant _____

3. robe/petit/blanc _____

4. ceinture/joli/brun _____

5. chaussettes/petit/bleu _____

6. manteau/grand/jaune _____

I. Draw a picture of your parents and describe them in French.

_____

_____

_____

_____

_____

_____

_____

_____

_____

LA VIE PRATIQUE

Select the best answer to the question based on what you read, and write its number in the space provided.

TOKIO KUMAGAÏ

Rue de Grenelle, TOKIO KUMAGAI conserve une ligne austère et confortable pour sa nouvelle collection de chaussures. Pour hommes : une ligne carrée et très virile. Pour femmes : une mise en valeur de la finesse du pied grâce au talon bobine et à l'élégance du daim. Les couleurs : Noir, marron, bordeaux, et des effets de drapé ou de vison, aussi originaux que ses dernières créations de prêt à porter.

What can you buy in this store?   _____

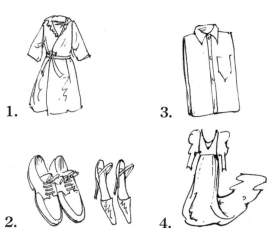

1.

2.

3.

4.

Leçon 9

A. Complete each sentence with an appropriate part of the body.

1. Je regarde avec _____.

2. J'écoute avec _____.

3. Je touche avec _____.

4. Je travaille avec _____.

5. Je marche avec _____.

6. Je danse avec _____.

7. Je parle avec _____.

8. Je porte un pantalon sur _____.

9. Je porte une écharpe *(scarf)* sur _____.

10. Je porte un chapeau sur _____.

B. Make sentences by choosing a word or phrase from each group.

J'		les cheveux longs
Marianne	ai	une grande bouche
Vous	ont	les yeux verts
Ils	avons	de longues jambes
Nous	a	une jolie figure
Georges	avez	bon cœur
Tu	as	un long nez
Anne et Cécile		de grandes oreilles

1. _____

2. _____

3. _____

49

4. _____

5. _____

6. _____

7. _____

8. _____

C. Write a four-sentence note in French to a friend describing your physical appearance.

_____

_____

_____

_____

_____

_____

D. Identify each person's problem.

1.   J'_____.

2.   Marie _____.

3.   Tu _____.

4.   Nous_____.

5.   Ils_____.

6.   Vous_____.

E. Say that these people don't have a problem anymore by making each of the sentences in Exercise D negative.

1. _____

2. _____

3. _____

4. _____

5. _____

6. _____

F. Describe these people who have an unusual physical appearance.

EXAMPLE: **René a de grands pieds.**

1. Philippe _____.

2. Les filles _____.

3. Ils _____.

4. Sylvie _____.

5. Tu _____.

6. Vous _____.

G. Write a list of four physical features you admire in a person.

1. _____

2. _____

3. _____

4. _____

H. Some people haven't been entirely honest about how old they are. Write out their correct ages in French.

EXAMPLE: (Mme Leblond 56/60)
Mme Leblond n'a pas cinquante-six ans. Elle a soixante ans.

1. (je 15/16) _____

_____

2. (M. Lesage 49/52) _____

_____

3. (vous 27/33) _____

_____

4. (tu 18/16) _____

_____

I. Answer these questions about yourself.

1. À quelle heure est-ce que tu as sommeil?

_____

2. Tu as quel âge?

_____

3. Combien de classes est-ce que tu as?

_____

4. Tu as les yeux de quelle couleur?

_____

_____

5. Tu as les cheveux de quelle couleur?

_____

6. Qu'est-ce que tu portes *(wear)* quand tu as froid?

_____

La Vie pratique

Select the best answer to the question, based on what you read, and write its number in the space provided.

LA BOXE

Dans tous les pays du monde, on éprouve le besoin de mettre au point et de populariser des techniques pour se défendre.

La boxe est un sport de combat réglementé où deux boxeurs s'opposent l'un à l'autre. Chaque participant a le droit de frapper la tête et le torse de son adversaire pour gagner des points ou le mettre hors de combat en le jetant à terre pour plus de dix secondes.

Dans la boxe anglaise, les adversaires se servent seulement de leurs poings pour attaquer et pour se défendre. **Dans la boxe française,** les deux boxeurs se battent à coups de poings et à coups de pied. Le pied peut frapper la figure et le corps de l'adversaire.

How is French boxing different from English boxing?   _____

1. In French boxing, boxers can hit each other with their heads.
2. In French boxing, boxers cannot hit the face of their opponents.
3. In French boxing, boxers can use their hands and their feet.
4. In French boxing, boxers can only use their hands.

Nom: _____ Classe: _____ Date: _____

Leçon 10

A. Express what the next day is.

1. C'est aujourd'hui mardi. Demain est_____.

2. C'est aujourd'hui vendredi. Demain est_____.

3. C'est aujourd'hui lundi. Demain est_____.

4. C'est aujourd'hui mercredi. Demain est_____.

5. C'est aujourd'hui dimanche. Demain est_____.

6. C'est aujourd'hui jeudi. Demain est_____.

7. C'est aujourd'hui samedi. Demain est_____.

B. Fill in the missing months.

1. janvier _____ **5.** mai_____ **9.** _____

2. _____ **6.** _____ **10.** _____

3. _____ **7.** juillet **11.** _____

4. _____ **8.** _____ **12.** décembre

C. Avant ou après? Give the day that comes before or after the day indicated.

1. le jour avant lundi _____

2. le jour après dimanche _____

3. le jour avant vendredi _____

55

Copyright © 2011 by AMSCO School Publications, Inc.

4. le jour avant mercredi   _____

5. le jour avant dimanche   _____

D. Write out in French all the circled dates.

EXAMPLE: **C'est aujourd'hui dimanche, le 6 octobre.**

	JANVIER	FÉVRIER	MARS	AVRIL
LUNDI	7 14 21 28	4 11 18 25	4 11 18 25	1 8 15 22 29
MARDI	1 8 15 22 29	5 12 19 26	5 12 19 26	2 9 16 23 30
MERCREDI	2 9 16 23 30	6 13 20 (27)	6 13 20 27	3 10 17 24
JEUDI	3 10 17 24 (31)	7 14 21 28	7 14 21 28	4 11 18 25
VENDREDI	4 11 18 25	1 8 15 22	1 (8) 15 22 29	5 12 19 26
SAMEDI	5 12 19 26	2 9 16 23	2 9 16 23 30	6 13 20 27
DIMANCHE	6 13 20 27	3 10 17 24	3 10 17 24 31	7 14 21 28

	MAI	JUIN	JUILLET	AOÛT
LUNDI	6 13 20 27	3 (10) 17 24	1 8 15 22 29	5 12 19 26
MARDI	7 14 21 28	4 11 18 25	2 9 (16) 23 30	6 13 20 27
MERCREDI	1 8 15 22 29	5 12 19 26	3 10 17 24 31	7 14 21 28
JEUDI	2 9 16 23 30	6 13 20 27	4 11 18 25	1 8 15 22 29
VENDREDI	3 10 17 (24) 31	7 14 21 28	5 12 19 26	2 9 16 23 30
SAMEDI	4 11 18 25	1 8 15 22 29	6 13 20 27	3 10 17 24 31
DIMANCHE	5 12 19 26	2 9 16 23 30	7 14 21 28	4 11 18 25

	SEPTEMBRE	OCTOBRE	NOVEMBRE	DÉCEMBRE
LUNDI	2 9 16 23 30	7 14 21 28	4 11 18 25	2 9 16 23 30
MARDI	3 10 17 24	1 8 15 22 29	5 12 19 26	3 10 17 24 31
MERCREDI	4 11 18 25	2 9 16 23 30	6 13 20 27	4 11 18 (25)
JEUDI	5 12 19 26	3 10 17 24 31	7 14 21 28	5 12 19 26
VENDREDI	6 13 20 27	4 11 18 25	(1) 8 15 22 29	6 13 20 27
SAMEDI	7 14 21 28	5 12 19 26	2 9 16 23 30	7 14 21 28
DIMANCHE	1 8 15 22 29	6 13 20 27	3 10 17 24	1 8 15 22 29

1. _____

2. _____

3. _____

4. _____

5. _____

6. _____

7. _____

8. _____

E. You are playing school with your younger cousin. Give her information by completing the following sentences.

1. Une année a _____ mois.

2. _____ est le premier (*first*) mois de l'année.

3. _____ est le dernier (*last*) mois de l'année.

4. Le mois de juin a _____ jours.

5. Il n'y a pas de classes le samedi et le _____.

6. Les grandes vacances sont en _____ et en _____.

7. Le jour de l'Indépendance est le quatre _____.

8. Le jour du Nouvel An est le premier _____.

F. Express these dates in French.

1. your birthday _____

2. your parents' birthdays _____

   _____

3. your brother's/sister's birthdays _____

   _____

4. New Year's Eve _____

5. Halloween _____

G. A friend you haven't seen in a while would like to see you. Write a note explaining what you do on specific days of the week.

_____

_____

_____

_____

_____

LA VIE PRATIQUE

Select the best answer to the question based on what you read, and write its number in the space provided.

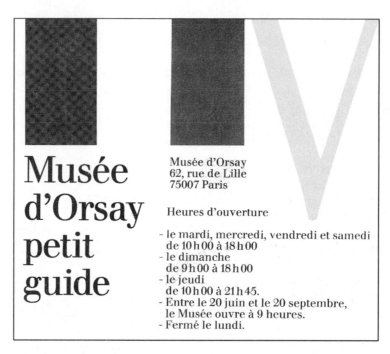

Musée d'Orsay
62, rue de Lille
75007 Paris

Heures d'ouverture

- le mardi, mercredi, vendredi et samedi
  de 10 h 00 à 18 h 00
- le dimanche
  de 9 h 00 à 18 h 00
- le jeudi
  de 10 h 00 à 21 h 45.
- Entre le 20 juin et le 20 septembre,
  le Musée ouvre à 9 heures.
- Fermé le lundi.

Musée d'Orsay petit guide

When can you visit the Musée d'Orsay in Paris?   _____

1. Only on Mondays.
2. Until 9 pm from June 20 to September 20.
3. Tuesday morning from 8 am to 10 am.
4. Thursdays from 10 am until 9:45 pm.

Leçon 11

A. Express the weather in the French cities on the map.

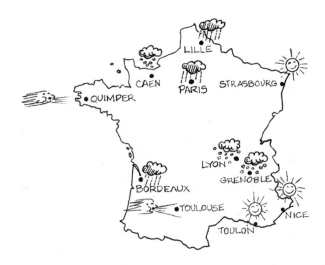

EXAMPLE: **À Quimper, il fait du vent.**

1. _____

2. _____

3. _____

4. _____

5. _____

6. _____

7. _____

8. _____

9. _____

10. _____

B. Quel temps fait-il? Answer the following questions in complete French sentences.

    1. Quel temps fait-il en été? _____

    _____

    2. Pendant quels mois fait-il chaud? _____

    _____

    3. Fait-il du soleil à midi? _____

    _____

    4. Quand est-ce qu'il neige? _____

    5. Pendant quels mois fait-il froid? _____

    _____

    6. Est-ce qu'il pleut beaucoup dans votre ville? _____

    _____

    7. Est-ce qu'il neige beaucoup dans votre ville? _____

    _____

    8. Il fait du vent en quelle saison? _____

    _____

    9. Qu'est-ce que vous faites quand il fait beau? _____

    _____

   10. Qu'est-ce que vous faites quand il fait mauvais? _____

    _____

C. Name the season and months for each picture.

    1.   saison _____

                             mois _____

                                  _____

2.   saison _____

mois _____

_____

3.   saison _____

mois _____

_____

4.   saison _____

mois _____

_____

D. Complete the sentence by expressing in which season you do the following activities.

1. Je fais un pique-nique _____.

2. Je joue au tennis _____.

3. Je joue au football américain_____.

4. Je joue dans la neige _____.

5. Je joue au base-ball _____.

6. Je fais une promenade au parc _____.

7. Je fais un voyage_____.

8. Je fais du ski _____.

E. Create sentences that tell what these people are doing.

faire attention	**faire une promenade**	**faire les devoirs**
faire du ski	**faire une partie de base-ball**	**faire une omelette**
faire un voyage	**faire un pique-nique**	

1. Je _____

2. Marie _____

3. Nous _____

4. Paul et Jacques _____

5. Tu _____

6. Il _____

7. Vous _____

8. Elles _____

F. Express that these people are not doing what they are supposed to be doing.

EXAMPLE: Jean/faire un voyage en Suisse
            Jean ne fait pas un voyage en Suisse.

1. Lisette/faire attention

    _____

2. je/faire mes devoirs

    _____

3. ils/faire le dîner

    _____

4. nous/faire la salade

    _____

5. tu/faire la valise (*suitcase*)

    _____

6. vous/faire la liste

    _____

G. For each picture identify the season, give the weather, and write one activity that you do at that time.

1. _____

   _____

   _____

   _____

2. _____

   _____

   _____

   _____

3. _____

   _____

   _____

   _____

4. _____

   _____

   _____

   _____

LA VIE PRATIQUE

Select the best answer to the question based on what you read, and write its number in the space provided.

Au pied des sommets enneigés de l'Atlas, la palme-raie sert d'écrin à une perle rouge : MARRAKECH. Un climat sec particulièrement sain ajoute encore au plaisir des visites et excursions, et permet la pratique de tous les sports de plein air (golf et tennis en premier lieu).

What is the weather like in Marrakech in Morocco?   _____

1. Too cold to go outside.
2. Too hot to play sports.
3. Windy and rainy.
4. Dry and comfortable.

Leçon 12

A. Identify the sports illustrated in the picture.

1. _____   6. _____

2. _____   7. _____

3. _____   8. _____

4. _____   9. _____

5. _____   10. _____

B. You are going to camp this summer and the camp questionnaire asks you to list your four favorite sports. Write your list.

1. _____ 3. _____

2. _____ 4. _____

C. Use the verb **faire** and **du** or **de la** to tell in which sports these people participate.

1. Je _____ natation.

2. Nous _____ patinage.

3. Tu _____ football.

4. Il _____ cyclisme.

5. Vous _____ gymnastique.

6. Elles _____ hockey.

D. Complete each sentence with the correct form of the verb that makes sense.

| remplir | saisir | choisir |
| applaudir | punir | finir |

1. Vous _____ des joueurs pour l'équipe.

2. Les spectateurs _____ le stade.

3. Je _____ le ballon.

4. _____ -tu après le match?

5. Nous _____ le match à quatre heures.

6. L'entraîneur _____ les joueurs qui n'écoutent pas.

E. Combine the elements to express what happens in M. Moreau's class.

    1. Le professeur/punir/les élèves

    _____

    2. Jeanne/remplir/le questionnaire

    _____

    3. Nous/applaudir

    _____

    4. Vous/saisir/le livre de Jacques

    _____

    5. Je/finir/tous les exercices

    _____

    6. Tu/choisir/la réponse correcte

    _____

    7. Les garçons/choisir/le bon exemple

    _____

    8. Vous/finir/le livre

    _____

F. Express what happens in class when M. Moreau is absent by giving the correct form of the verb in the negative.

EXAMPLE: (finir)/Nous/la leçon **Nous ne finissons pas la leçon.**

    1. (finir) Les filles _____ les exercices.

    2. (applaudir) Le directeur _____ la classe.

    3. (remplir) Vous _____ la liste de vocabulaire.

    4. (choisir) Les élèves _____ de faire attention.

G. Ask what each of the following people is doing by using inversion.

faire du football	gagner la compétition	remplir le stade
jouer au base-ball	finir le match	applaudir le gagnant *(winner)*

1. (elles) _____

2. (vous) _____

3. (nous) _____

4. (tu) _____

5. (ils) _____

6. (nous) _____

H. Ask questions about your classmates by changing the sentences to questions using inversion.

1. Il parle bien français.

_____

2. Il gagne le match.

_____

3. Elle joue au tennis le samedi.

_____

4. Elle fait beaucoup de sport.

_____

5. Il finit ses devoirs

_____

6. Elle applaudit l'acteur.

_____

7. Il danse bien.

_____

8. Elle travaille dans une boutique.

_____

I. Ask questions using inversion to find out what these people are doing.

    1. (jouer au basket-ball) Michel _____

    2. (regarder le match) Les filles _____

    3. (écouter le professeur) Isabelle _____

    4. (choisir la natation) Les étudiants _____

    5. (applaudir l´équipe) Les parents _____

    6. (remplir la liste) Le directeur _____

J. Using the clues given, form questions with **est-ce que** and with inversion.

    1. (comment) il joue au golf

    _____

    _____

    2. (où) tu pratiques la natation

    _____

    _____

    3. (qui) elles punissent

    _____

    _____

    4. (que) Pierre gagne

    _____

    _____

    5. (quand) vous arrivez à Paris.

    _____

    _____

6. (pourquoi) nous applaudissons?

_____

_____

LA VIE PRATIQUE

Select the best answer to the question based on what you read, and write its number in the space provided.

SKI - VOL
LA PASSION DE LA GLISSE

PLANCHE À VOILE
PARACHUTE
PENTAGLISS
SKI NAUTIQUE
TOBOGGAN

Plage du Larvotto - MONTE-CARLO
© **93.50.86.45**

On pratique ces sports de glisse quand   _____

1. il neige.
2. il pleut.
3. il fait froid.
4. il fait beau.

Leçon 13

A. Express which musical instrument each member of the Ricard family prefers.

1.

2.

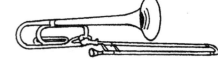

3.

4.

5.

6.

1. M. Ricard préfère _____.

2. Les grands-parents préfèrent _____.

3. Henriette préfère _____.

4. Jean et Luc préfèrent _____.

5. Maman préfère _____.

6. Les enfants préfèrent _____.

B. Write what each person is doing.

1. tu/attendre Robert

_____

2. nous/descendre du train

_____

3. ils/entendre la musique

_____

4. vous/répondre à la question

_____

5. je/entendre la fanfare

_____

6. elle/vendre des rafraîchissements (*refreshments*)

_____

C. Fill in the correct form of the verb that makes sense in the sentence.

attendre   **entendre**   **descendre**   **vendre**   **répondre**

1. Le musicien _____ aux questions.

2. J'_____ le commencement du concert.

3. _____ -vous la musique?

4. Ils _____ l'escalier.

5. _____ -tu la radio?

6. Vous _____ vos amis après le concert.

7. Le magasin _____ des CD.

8. Je _____ de l'autobus.

9. Nous _____: «oui».

10. M. Dupont et son frère _____ des instruments de musique.

D. Tell what these people are not doing by making the sentence negative.

    1. (entendre)   Tu _____ la musique.

    2. (descendre) Vous _____ en ville.

    3. (attendre)   Je _____ le bus.

    4. (vendre)   Ils _____ de CD.

    5. (répondre)   Nous _____ au téléphone.

    6. (attendre)   Elle _____ son ami.

E. Using inversion, form questions asking what each of the indicated subjects is doing.

    EXAMPLE: (elles/attendre leurs amis) **Attendent-elles leurs amis?**

    1. (nous/vendre des CD) _____

    2. (il/attendre le vendeur) _____

    3. (ils/entendre la musique) _____

    4. (tu/descendre au magasin) _____

    5. (vous/répondre rapidement) _____

    6. (elle/vendre des guitares) _____

F. Write a list of four musical gifts you could purchase for a family member or friend.

    1. _____   **3.** _____

    2. _____   **4.** _____

G. Write four sentences in French telling about the type of music you like, and why.

_____

_____

_____

_____

_____

LA VIE PRATIQUE

Select the best answer to the question based on what you read, and write its number in the space provided.

En avant la musique !

Du 15 au 20 septembre, tu vas en avoir plein les oreilles au 14ᵉ Salon international de la musique. Plus de 10 000 instruments attendent que tu les essayes. Mais si tu préfères les vidéo-clips, tu verras les meilleurs.

— Et puis, va vite à la page 84 de ton journal... un concours y est organisé. Le thème : la musique, bien sûr.

50 000 € de prix à gagner ! Et Picsou sera au Salon pour t'aider... Alors, fonce à la Grande Halle de la Villette, porte de Pantin !

What does this ad invite you to do?   _____

   1. Join a band.   **3.** Compose your own song.
   2. Enter a contest.   **4.** Make a music video.

Leçon 14

A. Match the animal with the phrase that describes it.

1. la vache _____
2. le cochon _____
3. l'oiseau _____
4. l'éléphant _____
5. l'âne _____
6. le renard _____
7. le lion _____
8. le chien _____
9. la poule _____
10. le mouton _____

a. Il est stupide.
b. Elle donne des œufs.
c. Elle donne du lait.
d. Il vole (*flies*).
e. C'est le roi (*king*) de la jungle.
f. Il est sale (*dirty*).
g. Il est très rusé (*sly*).
h. Il est grand et gris.
i. Il donne de la laine.
j. C'est le meilleur (*best*) ami de l'homme.

B. You are at the zoo. Tell your friend what to do.

EXAMPLE: trouver les chiens   **Trouve les chiens!**

1. regarder les animaux _____
2. applaudir les singes _____
3. saisir le lapin _____
4. donner à manger à l'éléphant _____

75

5. parler au lion _____

6. écouter le tigre _____

7. chercher les oiseaux_____

8. trouver les loups _____

9. admirer le renard _____

10. attendre les chevaux _____

C. Now tell your friend not to do certain things.

EXAMPLE: **Ne cherche pas les lapins!**

1. saisir les animaux _____

2. donner à manger aux tigres_____

3. répondre aux chats _____

4. punir les chiens _____

5. attendre les lions _____

6. parler aux éléphants _____

7. danser avec (*with*) les loups _____

_____

8. chanter avec les oiseaux _____

_____

9. jouer avec les singes_____

10. vendre les animaux _____

D. Mots croisés

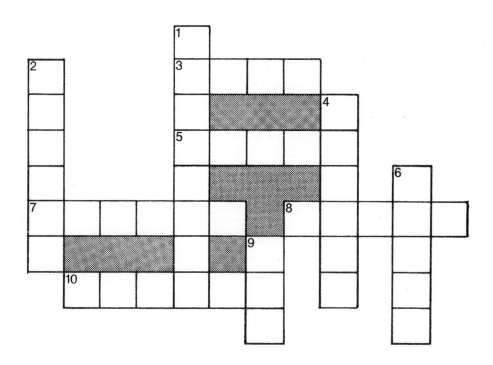

HORIZONTALEMENT

3. lion
5. hen
7. bird
8. cow
10. sheep

VERTICALEMENT

1. elephant
2. pig
4. fox
6. dog
9. donkey

E. Write the advice that M. and Mme Dumard give to their sons.

EXAMPLE: écouter en classe   **Écoutez en classe!**

1. regarder le tableau   _____

2. écouter le professeur   _____

3. finir les exercices   _____

4. répondre aux questions _____

5. choisir les réponses correctes _____

6. attendre la cloche (*bell*) _____

F. Write what the Dumard tell their sons not to do.

EXAMPLE: parler espagnol   **Ne parlez pas espagnol!**

1. parler en classe _____

2. attendre vos amis _____

3. punir le professeur _____

4. écouter les éléves _____

5. arriver en retard _____

6. applaudir _____

G. Write what suggestions your friends make for today.

EXAMPLE: regarder la télévision   **Regardons la télévision!**

1. travailler au marché_____

2. jouer au tennis _____

3. finir nos devoirs_____

4. écouter la musique classique_____

5. vendre les disques _____

6. descendre en ville _____

H. It's raining outside. You're also very tired. Tell your friends what you shouldn't do by changing your suggestions in Exercise G to the negative.

EXAMPLE: **Ne regardons pas la télévision!**

1. _____

2. _____

3. _____

4. _____

4. _____

5. _____

6. _____

I. Make a list of four things you want to tell your brother/sister not to do.

1. _____

2. _____

3. _____

4. _____

J. Write a four-sentence note to your parents suggesting what you and your family can do this evening.

_____

_____

_____

_____

_____

_____

_____

LA VIE PRATIQUE

Select the best answer to the question based on what you read, and write its number in the space provided.

Which proverb means: When nobody is around to watch you, you can do what you want.   ———————

1. Il faut appeler un chat un chat.
2. Il ne faut pas tuer la poule aux œufs d'or.
3. La nuit tous les chats sont gris.
4. Quand le chat n'est pas là, les souris dansent.

Leçon 15

A. M. Leclerc drives a taxi. Express in French where he drops off his customers.

EXAMPLE:

au théâtre **à l'hôpital** **à la maison**

1. _____ 2. _____

3. _____ 4. _____

5. _____ 6. _____

7. _____   8. _____

9. _____   10. _____

B. Imagine that your French-speaking pen pal comes to visit. List four places he/she might visit in your town.

1. _____   3. _____

2. _____   4. _____

C. There is a conference at the convention center. Tell from where these people are arriving.

EXAMPLE: **Lise arrive du zoo.**

1. M. Savin arrive _____

2. Mme Lanvin arrive _____

3. Mlle Constant arrive _____

4. Liliane arrive _____

5. Grégoire arrive _____

6. M. Bernard arrive _____

7. Mme Bernadot arrive _____

8. Mlle Nalet arrive _____

9. Arthur arrive _____

10. Marthe arrive _____

11. M. Grévisse arrive _____

12. Mme Lelong arrive _____

D. Express what the tourists are talking about.

EXAMPLE: **Ils parlent du café.**

1. _____

_____

2. _____

_____

3. _____

_____

4. _____

_____

5. _____

_____

6. _____

_____

7. _____

_____

8. _____

_____

E. Identify the place in French by combining the elements.

> EXAMPLE: (café/airport) **C'est le café de l'aéroport.**

1. (library/school)_____

_____

2. (factory/family Caron) _____

_____

3. (apartment/Véronique)_____

_____

4. (train station/city) _____

_____

5. (restaurant/hotel) _____

_____

F. Your Canadian pen pal, Jean, is curious about your town. Answer his questions about it.

JEAN: Comment est ta ville? _____

VOUS: _____
(Say whether it is big or small.)

JEAN: Il y a combien d'écoles dans ta ville? _____

VOUS: _____
(Tell how many there are.)

JEAN: Quels sont les cinémas populaires? _____

VOUS: _____
(Tell what they are.)

Jean: Que fais-tu pour t'amuser *(For fun)*? _____

VOUS: _____
(Tell what you do.)

Jean: Quel temps fait-il maintenant dans ta ville? _____

VOUS: _____

     (*Tell what it is like.*)

LA VIE PRATIQUE

Select the best answer to the question based on what you read, and write its number in the space provided.

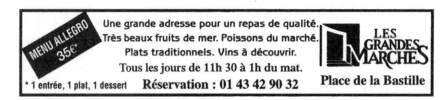

Où êtes-vous?   _____

    1. au marché.
    2. dans un magasin de fruits.
    3. dans un restaurant.
    4. dans un hôtel.

Leçon 16

A. Andrée has a lot of chores to do today. Express at what time she arrives at each destination.

EXAMPLE: **Elle arrive au supermarché à huit heures.**

1. _____

2. _____

3. _____

4. _____

5. _____

6. _____

7. _____

8. _____

B. Tell where these people are going.

EXAMPLE: Luc/pharmacie **Luc va à la pharmacie.**

1. je/église _____

2. ils/restaurant _____

3. nous/aéroport _____

4. Marianne/librairie _____

5. vous/boulangerie _____

6. Grégoire/hôtel _____

7. tu/grands magasins ____________________

8. Lise et Renée/lycée ____________________

C. Ask if these people are going to the stores indicated.

EXAMPLE: Henri/boutique **Va-t-il à la boutique?**

1. tu/pharmacie ____________________

2. nous/épicerie ____________________

3. les Caron/boulangerie ____________________

4. Laure/boucherie ____________________

5. vous/marché ____________________

6. Anne et Sylvie/magasins ____________________

D. Answer all the questions in Exercise C in the negative.

EXAMPLE: **Il ne va pas à la boutique.**

1. ____________________

2. ____________________

3. ____________________

4. ____________________

5. ____________________

6. ____________________

E. List four places that you go to frequently.

1. ____________________ 3. ____________________

2. ____________________ 4. ____________________

F. Some stores are closed today. Tell your friend not to go there.

EXAMPLE: **Ne va pas au grand magasin!**

1. _____

2. _____

3. _____

4. _____

5. _____

6. _____

G. Tell your brother or sister where he/she must go today.

EXAMPLE: **Va à la boucherie!**

1. _____

2. _____

3. _____

4. _____

5. _____

6. _____

H. Express what these people are going to do in their spare time.

EXAMPLE: **Elle va danser.**

1. Je _____

2. Anne _____

3. Nous _____

4. Paul et Henri _____

5. Vous _____

6. Tu _____

I. Ask if these people are going to do the following things.

    EXAMPLE: tu/aller au magasin **Vas-tu aller au magasin?**

  1. tu/travailler au supermarché

    _____

  2. il/étudier le vocabulaire

    _____

  3. elle/aller à la pharmacie

    _____

  4. vous/finir vos devoirs

    _____

  5. elles/faire l'exercice

    _____

  6. ils/préparer la mousse au chocolat

    _____

J. Your friend wants to know what you are going to do this summer. Write him/her a four-sentence note explaining your plans.

    _____

    _____

    _____

    _____

    _____

LA VIE PRATIQUE

Select the best answer to the question based on what you read, and write its number in the space provided.

ARRIVAGE Air France frais
Poulet grains, Pintade, Pigeon
Canard, Caille, Lapin, Coquelet....

On va à la _____ pour acheter ces produits.

1. boulangerie
2. boucherie
3. pharmacie
4. pâtisserie

Leçon 17

A. Here is a plan of the house built by Jacques Laplanche. Identify what you see in the picture.

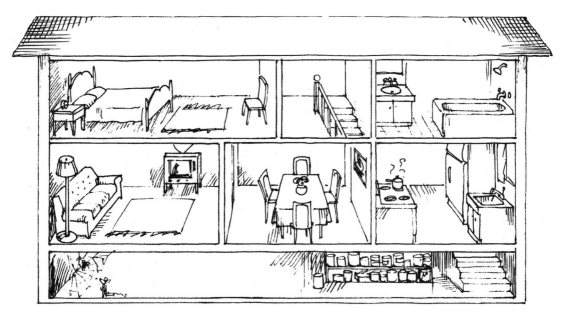

EXAMPLE: **C'est la chambre.**

1. _____   6. _____

2. _____   7. _____

3. _____   8. _____

4. _____   9. _____

5. _____   10. _____

B. List four items that you have in your bedroom.

1. _____   3. _____

2. _____   4. _____

95

C. Write a list of things you would expect to find in the following rooms.

LA CUISINE	LA SALLE À MANGER	LE SÉJOUR
_____	_____	_____
_____	_____	_____
_____	_____	_____
_____	_____	_____

D. Answer the questions about your apartment or house by using a preposition.

1. Où est la télé?

2. Où est la salle de bains?

3. Où est le réfrigérateur?

4. Où est la lampe?

5. Où est le séjour?

E. Write a list of six places where you might have left the CD you can't find.

EXAMPLE: **sous le lit**

1. _____   4. _____

2. _____   5. _____

3. _____   6. _____

F. Where is the cat hiding?

EXAMPLE: **Il est sous le lit.**

1. _____

2. _____

3. _____

4. _____

5. _____

6. _____

7. _____

8. _____

G. You have just moved to a new house or apartment. Write a note in French to a friend describing your new house.

_____

_____

_____

_____

_____

LA VIE PRATIQUE

Select the best answer to the question based on what you read, and write its number in the space provided.

AVENUE RODIN
Près HENRI MARTIN.Style
Mew's Anglais.Atelier
duplex 100 m2,2 caves,
entrée privative.Parfait
état,cuis. équipée.
Voie privée calme.
500.000 €. Direct Part.
préférence à Part.
Tél 49.53.00.50.

What does this ad say about this apartment? _____

1. It is very quiet.
2. The kitchen needs work.
3. It has a large entrance.
4. It has two bedrooms.

Leçon 18

A. Robert has won the lottery and is on a shopping spree. Express what items he chooses.

EXAMPLE: **Il choisit cette télévision à écran plat.**

1. _____

2. _____

3. _____

4. _____

5. _____

99

6. _____

7. _____

8. _____

B. Annette is having a party and wants her friends' opinions. Finish her question with the correct form of the demonstrative adjective **ce, cette, cet, ces**.

Que penses-tu de . . .

1. _____ robe?

2. _____ dîner?

3. _____ invitation?

4. _____ décorations?

5. _____ garçon?

6. _____ filles?

7. _____ CD?

8. _____ chaussures?

9. _____ lecteur de DVD?

10. _____ appareil photo numérique?

11. _____ sandwiches?

12. _____ orangeade?

13. _____ iPod?

14. _____ télévision à écran plat

15. _____ téléphone sans fil?

16. _____ mobile?

17. _____ four à micro-ondes?

18. _____ caméscope ?

19. _____ salade?

20. _____ gâteau?

C. Make a list of the five electronic devices you think are the most useful.

1. _____

2. _____

3. _____

4. _____

5. _____

D. Describe what the customers say about the electronic equipment.

EXAMPLE: four à micro-ondes/moderne   **Ce four à micro-ondes est moderne.**

1. ordinateur de poche/excellent _____

_____

2. mini-console de jeux vidéo /superbe _____

_____

3. téléphone mobile/extraordinaire _____

_____

4. lecteur de DVD/chouette _____

_____

5. calculateur solaire/démodé (*outdated*) _____

_____

6. caméscope/populaire _____

_____

E. Using adjectives that you have learned, write a list of four reasons why you like or dislike a computer.

1. _____

2. _____

3. _____

4. _____

LA VIE PRATIQUE

Select the best answer to the question based on what you read, and write its number in the space provided.

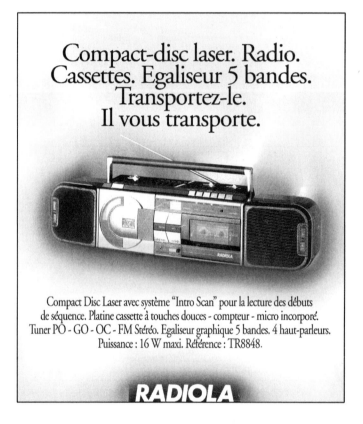

Compact-disc laser. Radio. Cassettes. Egaliseur 5 bandes. Transportez-le. Il vous transporte.

Compact Disc Laser avec système "Intro Scan" pour la lecture des débuts de séquence. Platine cassette à touches douces - compteur - micro incorporé. Tuner PO - GO - OC - FM Stéréo. Egaliseur graphique 5 bandes. 4 haut-parleurs. Puissance : 16 W maxi. Référence : TR8848.

RADIOLA

What's not true about this CD player? _____

1. It's portable.
2. It plays cassettes.
3. It can play five CDs
4. It is also a radio.

Leçon 19

A. Jeanne is preparing many dishes for a party, and she can't seem to find all the ingredients she needs. Her brother is helping her. Express what he finds.

EXAMPLE: **Voici le jambon.**

1. _____

2. _____

3. _____

4. _____

5. _____

6. _____

7. _____

8. _____

9. _____

10. _____

11. _____

12. _____

B. List six of your favorite foods.

1. _____   4. _____

2. _____   5. _____

3. _____   6. _____

C. List four foods that you don't like.

1. _____   3. _____

2. _____   4. _____

D. Express what is on the school menu for lunch.

EXAMPLE: **Il y a de la viande.**

1. _____

2. _____

3. _____

4. _____

5. _____

6. _____

7. _____

8. _____

9. _____

10. _____

11. _____

12. _____

E. Answer these questions about yourself in complete sentences.

1. Quand vous avez faim, que mangez-vous? _____

_____

2. Quand vous avez soif, qu'est-ce que vous aimez boire? _____

_____

3. Aimez-vous les fruits? _____

_____

4. Aimez-vous les légumes? _____

_____

5. Aimez-vous préparer des desserts? _____

_____

6. Quel est votre dessert préféré? _____

_____

F. You are in a restaurant with your friend Roger, who loves to eat a lot. Express what he says to the waiter.

EXAMPLE: **Donnez-moi de la glace, s'il vous plaît.**

1. _____

2. _____

3. _____

4. _____

5. _____

6. _____

7. _____

8. _____

9. _____

10. _____

G. Your local supermarket hasn't had a delivery in a long time. Express what is missing from the shelves.

EXAMPLE: soupe   **Il n'y a pas de soupe.**

1. fruits _____

2. poisson_____

3. bifteck _____

4. œufs _____

5. pain _____

6. laitue _____

7. épinards _____

8. haricots verts _____

9. fromage _____

10. tomates _____

H. Invite a friend for dinner. Tell him/her which day and what time to come, and also what you are going to make.

_____

_____

_____

_____

_____

_____

_____

_____

_____

_____

LA VIE PRATIQUE

You are in a hotel in Canada and you're getting breakfast in bed from room sevice. Look at the menu and make a list of what you would like to order.

_____

_____

_____

_____

_____

_____

_____

_____

_____

_____

_____

_____

_____

_____

_____

_____

_____

_____

_____

_____

LE PETIT DÉJEUNER

SERVICE AUX CHAMBRES

De 6h30 à 11h

Veuillez suspendre à la poignée extérieure de votre porte avant 2h.

N° de chambre .... Nombre de personnes ....

Nom ....
(En lettres moulées s.v.p.)

S.V.P. indiquez l'heure de livraison voulue

6h30-7h00 ☐   7h30-8h00 ☐   8h30-9h00 ☐   9h30-10h00 ☐   10h30-11h00 ☐
7h00-7h30 ☐   8h00-8h30 ☐   9h00-9h30 ☐   10h00-10h30 ☐

S.V.P. indiquez le nombre de commandes désirées.

Le Parisien

6.25

Jus

.... Orange   .... Pamplemousse   .... Tomate

.... Pain grillé   .... Croissants   .... Danoises

Le Canadien

11.00

Jus frais, deux oeufs cuits à votre façon,
servis avec pommes Rosti,
avec choix de bacon, saucisses, ou jambon, rôties

Frits ☐   Pochés ☐   Brouillés ☐

Le tout servi avec beurre et:

☐ Confiture de fraises   ☐ Marmalade
☐ Confiture de framboises   ☐ Miel
☐ Café   ☐ Thé   ☐ Lait

Servi avec: ☐ Lait   ☐ Crème   ☐ Citron

Boissons

... Petit thermos de café ou ... Café décaféiné ou ... Thé 3.75

... Chocolat chaud ou ... Lait ou ... Lait écrémé 2.00

Avec ☐ Lait   ☐ Crème   ☐ Citron

Un supplément de $2.00 sera ajouté à toutes les commandes.

Le Grand HÔTEL

10% de taxe provinciale non inclus.

UCCC/CD/NN

Leçon 20

A. Complete with the proper form of **vouloir**.

1. Je _____ un verre d'eau.

2. _____ -vous un sandwich au rosbif?

3. Luc et Pascal _____ mettre le couvert.

4. Nous ne _____ pas d'assiette.

5. Est-ce que tu _____ préparer la salade?

6. Elles ne _____ pas aller au pique-nique.

7. Vous _____ une tasse de café.

8. _____ -il du gâteau au chocolat?

B. Using the correct form of the verb **vouloir**, tell what everyone wants.

EXAMPLE: je/de l'orangeade   **Je veux de l'orangeade.**

1. Louis/du thon

_____

2. nous/des œufs durs

_____

3. Marie et Alice/des cerises

_____

4. tu/une fourchette

_____

5. je/des pommes de terre

_____

6. vous/une tasse

_____

7. ils/des saucisses

_____

8. elle/une assiette

_____

9. tu/un sandwich

_____

10. nous/des chips

_____

C. The students in the École Gastronomique are learning to become chefs. State what dishes they can prepare.

rosbif	**poulet**	**salade niçoise**
bifteck	**bouillabaisse**	**pommes de terre**
poisson	**œufs**	**soupe**

EXAMPLE: **Il peut préparer de la soupe.**

1. Nous _____.

2. Marc et Jean _____.

3. Anne _____.

4. Je _____.

5. Louise et Micheline _____.

6. Tu _____.

7. Paul _____.

8. Vous _____.

D. What can't they do? Change your answers to Exercise C to the negative.

EXAMPLE: **Je ne peux pas préparer de soupe.**

1. _____
2. _____
3. _____
4. _____
5. _____
6. _____
7. _____
8. _____

E. Pierre is participating in a food-eating contest. Express what he says he can eat by using a form of **tout**.

EXAMPLE: **Je peux manger tous les petits pois.**

1. _____

2. _____

3. _____

4. _____

5. _____

6. _____

7. _____

8. _____

F. You're having company for dinner. Write a note to your younger brother explaining how to set the table. You may use the command: **Mets** (*Put*).

_____

_____

_____

_____

_____

LA VIE PRATIQUE

How would you express this proverb in English?   _____
Vouloir, c'est pouvoir.

1. Necessity is the mother of invention.
2. All's well than ends well.
3. Nothing ventured nothing gained.
4. Where there's a will, there's a way.

Leçon 21

A. Fill in the missing letters for each country. Then join the letters to find out where Marie is going for her vacation.

1. H ___ ï t i

2. J a p o ___

3. E s p a ___ n e

4. A l ___ e m a g n ___

5. É ___ a t s - U n i s

6. C h i n ___

7. ___ u s s i e

8. F ___ a n c e

9. I t a l i ___

Marie va en _____.

B. From the information on the maps, write the French names of the countries indicated. Use the appropriate article.

1. _____

2. _____

3. _____

4. _____

115

5. _____

6. _____

7. _____

8. _____

9. _____

10. _____

C. Express where these people are from by completing the sentences with **du**, **d'**, **de**, or **des**.

1. Je suis _____ États-Unis.

2. Il est _____ Russie.

3. Nous sommes _____ Italie.

4. Vous êtes _____ France.

5. Tu es _____ Espagne.

6. Ils sont _____ Angleterre.

7. Elle est _____ Chine.

8. Elles sont _____ Japon.

9. Vous êtes _____ Canada.

10. Tu es _____ Allemagne.

D. By looking at the pictures, tell the nationality of the people mentioned.

1. Luigi est _____

2. Mireille est_____

3. Dimitri est_____

4. Ces femmes sont _____

5. Juan est _____

6. Max est _____

E. Describe the people you know by supplying the correct forms of the adjectives.

1. (haïtien)   Les garçons sont _____.

2. (italien)   Mario est _____.

3. (canadien)   Claudine est _____.

4. (français)   Sylvie est _____.

5. (anglais) Les grands-pères sont _____.

6. (chinois) Anne est _____.

7. (mexicain) Les jeunes filles sont _____.

8. (japonais) Marie est _____.

9. (américain) Les mères sont _____.

10. (haïtien) Marie-Pierre est _____.

F. You are at an International Youth Congress. All delegates have to write three sentences about themselves and their origins. Express what each person writes.

EXAMPLE: Douglas/Canada/Canadian
Je m'appelle Douglas. Je suis du Canada. Je suis canadien.

1. Mariko/Japan/Japanese

   _____

2. Gabrielle/Haiti/Haitian

   _____

3. Maria/Italy/Italian

   _____

4. Carmen/Spain/Spanish

   _____

5. Steve/U.S./American

   _____

6. Heidi/Germany/German

   _____

7. Janine/France/French

   _____

8. Madeleine/Canada/Canadian

   _____

G. Describe the nationalities of these students.

    EXAMPLE: Joan/États-Unis **Joan est américaine.**

1. Jean-Paul et Pierre/France

_____

2. Luis et Pablo/Espagne

_____

3. Natasha/Russie

_____

4. Victoria/Angleterre

_____

5. Réginald et Patrick/Haïti

_____

6. Marie-Hélène/Canada

_____

7. Vincenza et Ana Maria/Italie

_____

8. Suyin (*f.*) et HoMing (*f.*)/Chine

_____

H. A friend of yours is curious about your French cousin. Write a four-sentence note to him/her describing your cousin and his/her background.

_____

_____

_____

LA VIE PRATIQUE

Select the best answer to the question based on what you read, and write its number in the space provided.

L'Université de Montréal, fondée en 1878, est la plus grande université française en Amérique du Nord. Depuis plus de 40 ans, l'Ecole de français offre des cours de français à une clientèle internationale intéressée par le Québec et ses caractéristiques socioculturelles.

What do you know about this school?   _____

1. It has 1878 students.
2. Most of the students are over 40 years old.
3. It accepts students from many different countries.
4. It has branches in many countries.

Leçon 22

A. Tell how these people go to work.

EXAMPLE: **Je prends un taxi.**

1. Les élèves _____

2. Philippe _____

3. Nous_____

4. Le docteur _____

121

5. Tu _____

6. Vous _____

B. Tell where you go to use the following means of transportation.

EXAMPLE: **Je vais à l'aéroport.**

1. Je vais _____

2. Je vais _____

3. Je vais _____

4. Je vais _____

C. Choose one element from each column to tell what means of transportation these people use.

Je		le bateau
Laure	prends	l'avion
Pierre et Luc	prenons	le train
Nous	prennent	le taxi
Les filles	prends	la voiture
Luc	prenez	le scooter
Tu	prend	l'autobus
Vous		la motocyclette

1. _____

2. _____

3. _____

4. _____

5. _____

6. _____

7. _____

8. _____

D. There's a lot of road construction going on. Tell your friends not to take the means of transportation shown in the pictures.

EXAMPLE: **Ne prenez pas la voiture.**

1. _____

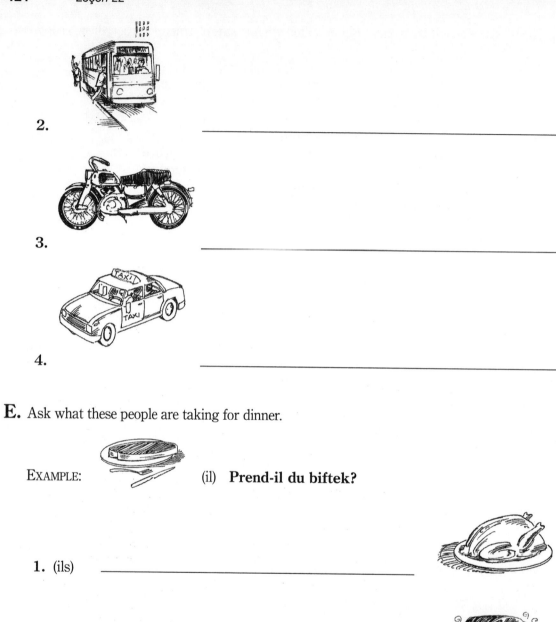

2. _____

3. _____

4. _____

E. Ask what these people are taking for dinner.

EXAMPLE: (il)   **Prend-il du biftek?**

1. (ils)   _____

2. (tu)   _____

3. (nous)   _____

4. (vous) _____

5. (elle) _____

6. (elles) _____

F. You're a fussy eater. Write a list of things you don't eat.

EXAMPLE: **Je ne prends pas de fruits.**

1. _____

2. _____

3. _____

4. _____

5. _____

6. _____

G. Tell what these people are or aren't learning to do.

EXAMPLE: **Non, je n'apprends pas la gymnastique.**

1. Oui, il _____

2. Oui, je _____

3. Non, nous _____

4. Oui, elles _____

5. Non, tu _____

6. Non, vous _____

H. Ask if these people understand the following languages.

    EXAMPLE: tu/russe **Comprends-tu le russe?**

    1. vous/anglais _____

    2. ils/français _____

    3. tu/allemand _____

    4. elle/chinois _____

    5. elles/italien _____

    6. il/espagnol _____

I. Your friend would like to go to school with you. Explain at what time you leave, how you go to school, with whom you go, and at what time you arrive.

_____

_____

_____

_____

_____

_____

_____

_____

_____

_____

_____

LA VIE PRATIQUE

Select the best answer to the question based on what you read, and write its number in the space provided.

BATOBUS. 01.44.11.33.99. Six escales pour retrouver l'esprit des quartiers parisiens en naviguant de l'un à l'autre: Tour Eiffel, St-Germain-des-Prés, Louvre, Hôtel-de-Ville, Notre-Dame, Musée d'Orsay. Un bateau toutes les 25mn à chaque escale. Tlj de 10h à 21h. Tarifs: 11€, –16 ans: 5€.

What is being described?   _____

1. A tour of Paris in a taxi?
2. A boat ride on the Seine River in Paris?
3. A trip by subway in Paris?
4. A guided tour of Paris in a tourist bus?

Leçon 23

A. There is no school today. Suggest to your friend where you might go.

EXAMPLE: **Allons au parc**!

1. _____

2. _____

3. _____

4. _____

5. _____

129

6. _____

7. _____

8. _____

9. _____

10. _____

B. List six places where you would like to go with your best friend on a Sunday afternoon.

1. _____   4. _____

2. _____   5. _____

3. _____   6. _____

C. Tell what each of these people can see from the observation tower.

EXAMPLE: (il/un jardin) **Il voit un jardin.**

1. (Roger/une église) _____

2. (tu/un cirque) _____

3. (les garçons/un stade) _____

4. (je/un musée) _____

5. (Nancy/une piscine) _____

6. (vous/un zoo) _____

7. (Élise et Carine/une discothèque) _____

_____

8. (nous/un théâtre) _____

D. Complete the sentences to tell what these people are photographing.

musée	zoo	parc
plage	match	piscine
jardin	cirque	

EXAMPLE: **Elle prend des photos du stade.**

1. Je _____

2. Paul _____

3. Nous _____

4. Anne et Lise _____

5. Tu _____

6. Les touristes _____

7. Vous _____

8. Marie-Claude _____

E. Some of your friends are talking about their summer plans. Express what they say by emphazising the subject.

EXAMPLE: Il va aller en Europe.   **Lui, il va aller en Europe.**

1. Il va travailler.

_____

2. Je vais étudier.

_____

3. Elles vont voyager.

_____

4. Tu vas aller en France.

_____

5. Elle va nager à la piscine.

_____

6. Vous allez jouer au tennis.

_____

7. Ils vont faire du cyclisme.

_____

8. Nous allons voir des amis.

_____

F. Some people can never find anything. Help them out by completing the sentences.

EXAMPLE: (*her*)   **Ton livre est à côté d'elle.**

1. (*us*) Ta chemise est chez _____.

2. (*you, familiar*) Ton cahier est près de _____.

3. (*me*) Tes CD sont en face de _____.

4. (*them, m.*) Ton frère est derrière _____.

5. (*you, formal*) Vos livres sont devant _____.

6. (*him*) Ton amie n'est pas loin de _____.

7. (*them, f.*) Ton chien est avec _____.

8. (*her*) Tes chats vont vers _____.

G. Answer these questions about the students in your class by giving a one-word answer.

EXAMPLE: (il)   Qui danse? **Lui.**

1. (*ils*) Qui parle français? _____.

2. (*elle*) Qui choisit la réponse correcte? _____.

3. (*je*) Qui travaille dur? _____.

4. (*nous*) Qui fait toujours attention? _____.

5. (*elles*) Qui ne comprend pas le professeur? _____.

6. (*tu*) Qui écoute toujours en classe? _____.

7. (*il*) Qui va fermer la porte? _____.

8. (*vous*) Qui prépare le dîner? _____.

H. Your friends are discussing what they want to see when they travel in and around Paris. Complete the subjects by filling in the blanks with the stress pronoun corresponding to the word in parentheses.

EXAMPLE: (*I*)   Jean et **moi**, nous voulons voir la tour Eiffel.

1. (*they, m.*) Roger et _____, ils veulent voir les Invalides.

2. (*I*) Anne et _____, nous voulons voir le Louvre.

3. (*you, familiar*) Éric et _____, vous voulez voir Versailles.

4. (*she*) Lucien et _____, ils veulent voir le Sacré-Cœur.

5. (*we*) Claude et _____, nous voulons voir Notre-Dame.

6. (*he*) Pierre et _____, ils veulent voir les Tuileries.

7. (*they, f.*) Lise et _____, elles veulent voir l'Arc de Triomphe.

8. (*you, formal*) Christophe et _____, vous voulez voir Montmartre.

I. Your pen pal is coming to visit from Martinique. Write a note in French telling him/her what things he/she can see in your city.

_____

_____

_____

_____

_____

_____

LA VIE PRATIQUE

Select the best answer to the question based on what you read, and write its number in the space provided.

CIRQUE JOSEPH BOUGLIONE 95-Herblay.
Terrain de la MJC. 06.80.11.11.98. Pl: 10 à 25 € Mer,
Dim 15h; Sam 15h, 20h30. Dernière le 20 juin:
Nouveau spectacle: avec tigres, Cavaleries, chameaux,
clowns, jongleurs, trapézistes, acrobates sur fil,
magiciens...

What can you see in this Parisian circus?   _____

1. jugglers
2. high-wire acts
3. clowns
4. ferocious animals
5. magicians
6. all of the above

Leçon 24

A. Express what these people are doing for the summer.

EXAMPLE: **je/aller chez mes cousins**   Je vais chez mes cousins.

1. nous/aller dans une colo _____

2. je/faire un voyage _____

3. les filles/aller à la montagne _____

4. Lucien/faire du camping _____

5. vous/rester à la maison _____

6. tu/faire des excursions _____

7. Marie-Ange/aller à la campagne _____

8. Robert et Marc/faire une randonnée _____

9. Éric et moi/aller à la mer _____

10. Michel et toi/visiter un pays étranger _____

_____

B. Write a list of what you would like to do for the summer. Begin your sentence with: **Je voudrais** (*I would like*).

1. _____

2. _____

3. _____

4. _____

5. _____

C. Tell what each of these people receives as a birthday gift.

EXAMPLE: Lucien/des livres   **Lucien reçoit des livres.**

1. Liliane/des vêtements

_____

2. je/de l'argent

_____

3. vous/des patins

_____

4. Paul et Georgette/des CD

_____

5. nous/des chemises

_____

6. Robert/un gant de base-ball

_____

7. tu/un vélo

_____

8. les filles/des jeux vidéo

_____

D. Ask how much money these classmates usually get for their allowance.

EXAMPLES: il/20   **Reçoit-il vingt dollars?**
            Pierre/16   **Est-ce que Pierre reçoit seize dollars?**

1. vous/$18 _____

2. Lucie/$17 _____

3. Odette et Paul/$15 _____

4. Hervé/$13_____

5. tu/$12 _____

6. Thomas et Richard/$14 _____

_____

E. Express how these people spent Sunday afternoon.

EXAMPLE: il/étudier **Il a étudié.**

1. nous/marcher dans le parc

_____

2. les garçons/jouer au football

_____

3. je/travailler au supermarché

_____

4. Alice/regarder la télévision

_____

5. Régine et Suzanne/écouter des CD

_____

6. tu/garder des enfants

_____

7. Georges/visiter des amis

_____

8. vous/manger au restaurant

_____

F. You went to a party and your parents ask you what you and your friends did there. Write your parents' questions using inversion.

EXAMPLES: (vous) **Avez-vous dansé?**
(Jean) **Jean a-t-il dansé?**

1. (Jacques) _____

2. (elles) _____

3. (tu) _____

4. (les garçons) _____

   _____

5. (ils) _____

6. (vous) _____

G. Write a note about how well you worked last year and what you are going to do to have fun this summer vacation.

_____

_____

_____

_____

_____

_____

LA VIE PRATIQUE

Select the best answer to the question based on what you read, and write its number in the space provided.

Les randonneurs d'Ile de France (RIF). Cette association de randonnées pédestres propose des sorties en groupe tous les jours. Un programme bimestriel vous donne le choix entre 300 sorties «à la carte» de tous niveaux proposées par une équipe de 150 animatrices et animateurs. Venez nous rendre visite.

LES RANDONNEURS D'ILE DE FRANCE
organisent toute l'année et tous les jours
des randonnées pédestres accompagnées
http://assoc.wanadoo.fr/rif.rando
☎ 01 45 42 24 72

Ces annonces intéressent les personnes qui _____

1. habitent sur une île.
2. nagent bien.
3. aiment marcher.
4. ont un ordinateur.